Dad's Grand Plan

Roderick Hunt   Alex Brychta

Characters

Narrator

Kipper

Biff

Chip

Mum

Floppy/Dad

Scene 1

Narrator Scene 1 'Dad's Grand Plan'
Everyone was excited.
It was holiday time.

Kipper I am getting excited.
Only two days to go.

Biff We are all getting excited.

Chip Even Floppy looks excited.

Kipper	Yes. He knows about the holiday.
Biff	Don't be silly, Kipper. Floppy doesn't know that.
Floppy	Grrrr! Hu-hu-hu!
Kipper	See! He does know.
Narrator	Mum came in. She gave a big sigh.

Chip   What's the matter, Mum?

Mum   It's Dad.
He's in a funny mood.
He wants a family meeting.

Kipper   A family meeting?
What's that?

Mum   He's got a Grand Plan.

Chip   A Grand Plan?

Biff   I don't like the sound of this.

Floppy   Grrrr! Huff! Huff!

Kipper   Nor does Floppy.

Narrator   Nobody liked the sound of a Grand Plan.

Scene 2

Narrator   Scene 2   'The family meeting'
Everyone sat at the table.

Dad   We go on holiday in two days.

Kipper   Yes, even Floppy is excited.

Biff   What is the Grand Plan?

Dad   I want everyone to help.

6

Narrator	Dad had a big sheet of paper.
Dad	I have made a list. Everyone has jobs to do.
Biff	Is this the Grand Plan?
Mum	Maybe it's a good idea. Nobody will get cross.
Chip	*(sighs)* I wonder about that.

Scene 3

Narrator	Scene 3 'Will the Grand Plan work?'
Biff	I've packed my bag.
Chip	I've packed my bag, too.
Kipper	I've almost packed my bag.
Biff	I've done all my jobs.
Kipper	So have I.

Dad	I have not packed yet.
Mum	Why not?
Dad	I can't find my socks.
Mum	They are in the washing machine.
Dad	*(crossly)* Why are they in there?
Mum	That was where you put them.
Chip	*(whispers)* Is Dad getting cross?

Narrator   At last all the jobs were done.
It was time to go.

Mum   Get in the car, everyone.

Dad   You see. My Grand Plan worked.
Nothing went wrong.
Nobody got cross.

Chip   *(whispers)*   There's still time.

Kipper	I don't want to sit in the middle.
Biff	You must. You are the smallest.
Kipper	*(crossly)* It's not fair!
Chip	It is fair!
Mum	Don't fight. You can take turns in the middle.
Dad	Remember my Grand Plan.

Scene 4

Narrator   Scene 4   'In the car'
Mum drove the car.
It was a hot day.

Kipper   I'm hot.

Chip   Can we stop for a drink?

Dad   No. It will make us late.

Biff   Why can't we stop now?

12

Kipper	Why can't we stop? I want to change seats.
Dad	We don't have time to stop.
Mum	Maybe we should stop.
Chip	Yes. I'm thirsty.
Biff	We are all thirsty.

(Dad sighs.)

Narrator   Mum saw a place to stop.

Mum   Let's stop here.
Floppy can have a run.

Biff   Where is Floppy?

Dad   He's in the back of the car.

Kipper   No. He's not in the back.

Chip   Oh no! We've forgotten Floppy.

Narrator	It was true. Floppy wasn't in the car.
Dad	Where is he?
Chip	He was in the back garden.
Mum	We'll have to go back for him.
Biff	*(sighs)* Oh no! So much for Dad's Grand Plan.

Scene 5

Narrator Scene 5 'Everyone gets cross'
They went back and got Floppy.

Biff Do we have to go so fast?

Kipper Slow down, Mum.
I feel sick.

Mum If I slow down, we'll never get there.

Chip   Poor old Floppy!
             He thought we'd never come back.

Floppy   *(panting)*   Uh-uh! Uh-uh! Uh-uh!

(There is a bumping noise.)

Biff   What was that?

Dad   *(gasps)*   Oh no!
             A bag has fallen off the roof rack.

Narrator   Mum stopped the car.
Everyone got out.

Kipper   I hope my bag hasn't fallen off.

Chip   The bag has come open.

Mum   There are clothes in the road.

Biff   They look like Dad's clothes.

Kipper	Dad's socks are in the road.
Biff	Dad's shirts are in the hedge.
Chip	*(laughs)* His pants are in a tree.
Narrator	Dad looked cross.
Dad	Don't stand there laughing. Help me pick up my clothes.
Mum	This wasn't in Dad's Grand Plan.

Scene 6

Narrator	Scene 6 'At the holiday cottage' At last they got to the cottage.
Mum	Here we are at last.
Chip	The cottage looks good.
Biff	Look! There is a little stream.
Kipper	There is a rope swing on that tree.

20

Dad	We are going to have a good time.
Narrator	Dad unlocked the door. Everyone went inside the cottage.
Biff	Oh no! Everything is black.
Dad	There is soot everywhere. It has come from the chimney.

Kipper   There is soot on the tables and chairs.

Chip   There is soot all over the floor.

(There is a cawing sound.)

Mum   What's that? It sounds like a bird.

Dad   Look! It's a crow.

Biff   How did it get into the cottage?

Mum	I think it flew down the chimney.

(There is a flapping sound.)

Kipper	It's frightened.
	Let it out.

Narrator	Dad caught the crow and let it out.
	Everyone felt sorry for it.

Biff	I'm glad it's gone.
	But what a mess it made!

Narrator Mum and Dad got buckets and cloths.

Mum We'll have to clean up all the soot.

Chip What a way to start the holiday.

Biff This wasn't in Dad's Grand Plan.

Dad Nor was having my pants in a tree!